MATHS TODAY
for ages 6-7

Addition

Subtraction

Multiplication

Division

Length

Fractions

Time

Money

Shape

Graphs

Addition

6 + 3 = ☐
7 + 2 = ☐
5 + 4 = ☐

3 + 4 = ☐
1 + 6 = ☐
2 + 5 = ☐

5 + 3 = ☐
4 + 4 = ☐
6 + 2 = ☐

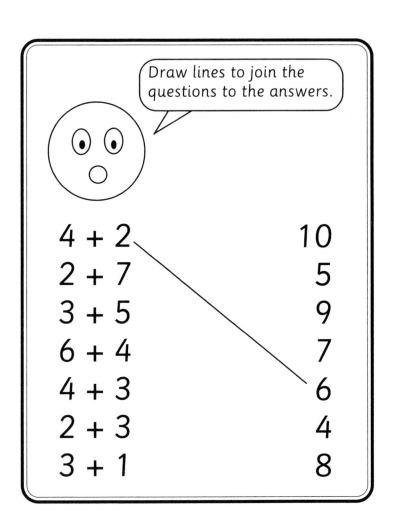

Draw lines to join the questions to the answers.

4 + 2	10
2 + 7	5
3 + 5	9
6 + 4	7
4 + 3	6
2 + 3	4
3 + 1	8

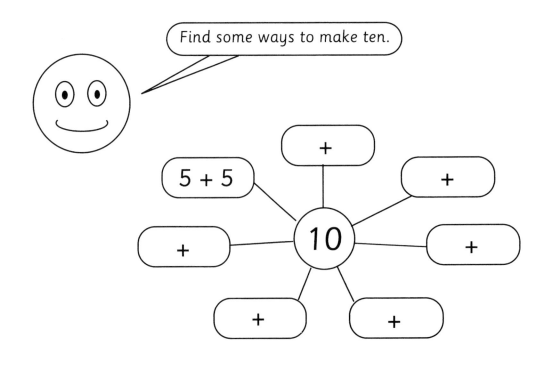

Find some ways to make ten.

5 + 5

+

+

+

+

10

+

+

Making 12

We can add numbers together to make 12 in lots of ways .

12

6 + 6 = 12

11 + 1 = 12   1 + 11 = 12

10 + 2 = 12   2 + 10 = 12

9 + 3 = 12   3 + 9 = 12

8 + 4 = 12   4 + 8 = 12

7 + 5 = 12   5 + 7 = 12

See how many ways you can make 11.

11

10 + 1 = 11   ☐ + ☐ = 11

9 + 2 = 11   ☐ + ☐ = 11

8 + 3 = 11   ☐ + ☐ = 11

7 + 4 = 11   ☐ + ☐ = 11

6 + 5 = 11   ☐ + ☐ = 11

Number Speed

Try to answer these questions as quickly as possible.

0 + 3 =

4 + 2 =

7 + 1 =

5 + 4 =

6 + 2 =

1 + 5 =

3 + 7 =

6 + 3 =

5 + 2 =

3 + 3 =

4 + 3 =

7 + 0 =

2 + 4 =

0 + 8 =

4 + 4 =

8 + 2 =

Subtraction

10 - 6 = ☐
10 - 8 = ☐
10 - 4 = ☐

8 - 3 = ☐
8 - 5 = ☐
8 - 2 = ☐

12 - 6 = ☐
12 - 4 = ☐
12 - 9 = ☐

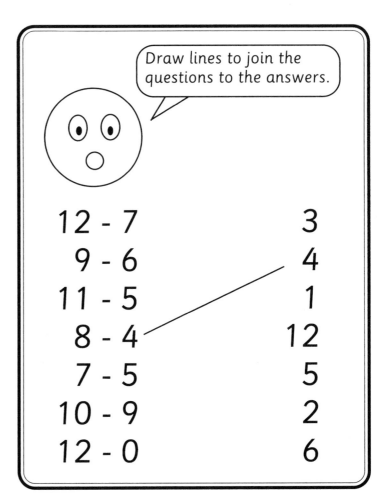

Draw lines to join the questions to the answers.

12 - 7   3
9 - 6   4
11 - 5   1
8 - 4   12
7 - 5   5
10 - 9   2
12 - 0   6

Try these subtractions from 9.

9 - 9 = ☐   9 - 8 = ☐

9 - 7 = ☐   9 - 6 = ☐

9 - 5 = ☐   9 - 4 = ☐

9 - 3 = ☐   9 - 2 = ☐

9 - 1 = ☐   9 - 0 = ☐

Count the stars and the circles.

How many stars are there?

There are ☐ stars.

How many circles are there?

There are ☐ circles.

How many more stars than circles are there?

There are ☐ more stars than circles.

There are ☐ stars and circles altogether.

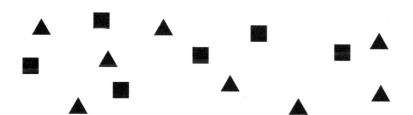

How many more triangles than squares are there?

There are ☐ more triangles than squares.

6 - 2 =

4 - 3 =

8 - 5 =

12 - 7 =

9 - 4 =

10 - 5 =

7 - 6 =

5 - 3 =

11 - 9 =

8 - 8 =

6 - 0 =

12 - 4 =

10 - 6 =

7 - 3 =

4 - 2 =

9 - 8 =

Time

What times are shown on the clocks?

4 o'clock

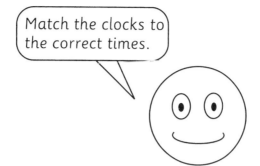

Match the clocks to the correct times.

Try to answer these questions as quickly as possible.

3 + 4 =

5 - 2 =

6 + 6 =

9 - 3 =

5 + 7 =

8 - 3 =

4 + 6 =

11 - 5 =

7 + 4 =

9 - 6 =

4 + 4 =

12 - 8 =

3 + 3 =

4 - 2 =

3 + 7 =

10 - 7 =

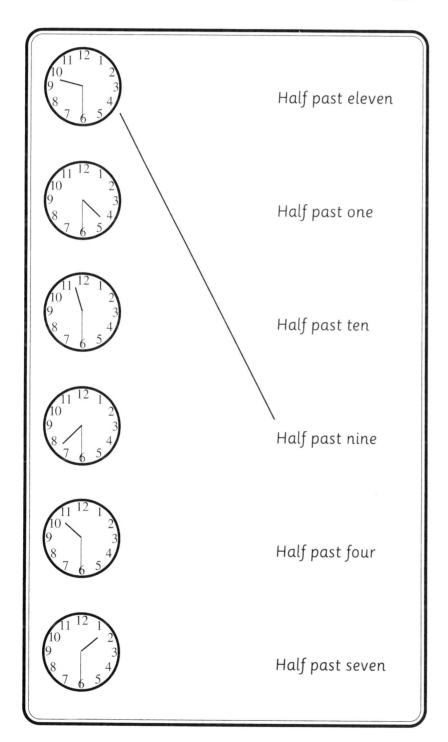

Half past eleven

Half past one

Half past ten

Half past nine

Half past four

Half past seven

Money

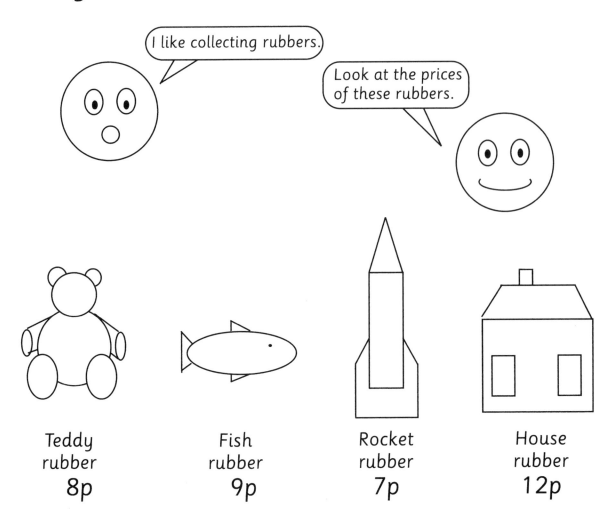

Teddy
rubber
8p

Fish
rubber
9p

Rocket
rubber
7p

House
rubber
12p

Which rubber is most expensive? _____

Which rubber is cheapest? _____

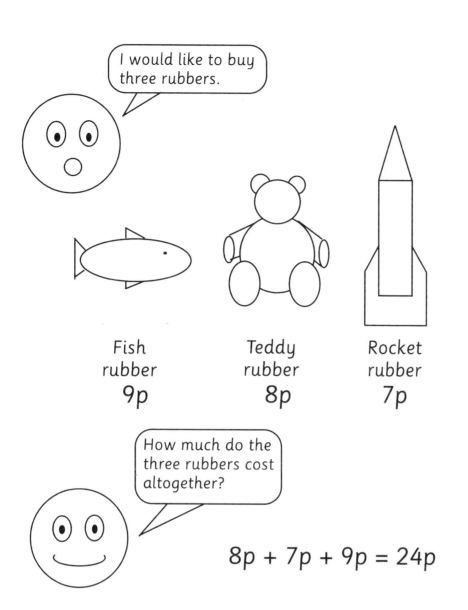

Fish
rubber
9p

Teddy
rubber
8p

Rocket
rubber
7p

$$8p + 7p + 9p = 24p$$

Try these money additions:

$$6p + 2p + 3p = \boxed{\qquad} p$$
$$5p + 3p + 2p = \boxed{\qquad} p$$
$$2p + 5p + 2p =$$
$$1p + 6p + 3p =$$
$$4p + 3p + 2p =$$

Number Speed

Try to answer these
questions as quickly
as possible.

$$6 + 7 =$$

$$8 + 9 =$$

$$7 + 4 =$$

$$8 + 6 =$$

$$9 + 5 =$$

$$8 + 8 =$$

$$10 + 7 =$$

$$7 + 9 =$$

$$12 + 8 =$$

$$11 + 6 =$$

$$9 + 9 =$$

$$4 + 12 =$$

$$10 + 8 =$$

$$7 + 12 =$$

$$6 + 5 =$$

$$8 + 7 =$$

More money

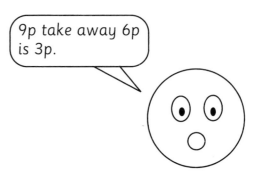

7p - 4p = ☐ p

8p - 3p = ☐ p

10p - 6p = ☐ p

8p - 7p = ☐ p

14p - 6p = ☐ p

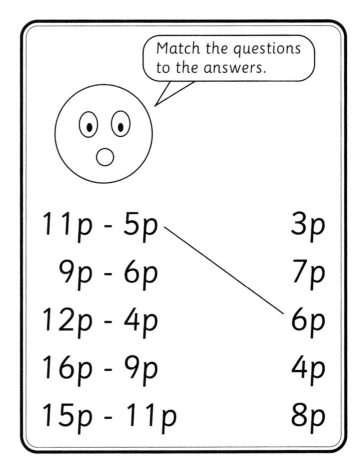

Match the questions to the answers.

11p - 5p	3p
9p - 6p	7p
12p - 4p	6p
16p - 9p	4p
15p - 11p	8p

Take away from 10p.

10p - 6p = ☐ p   10p - 3p = ☐ p

10p - 5p = ☐ p   10p - 2p = ☐ p

10p - 7p = ☐ p   10p - 8p = ☐ p

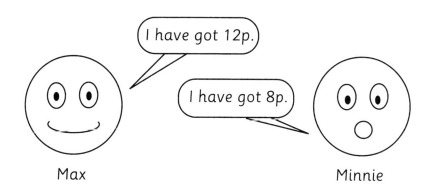

Max

Minnie

Max has got 12p.
Minnie has got 8p.

How much money have Max
and Minnie got altogether? [ ] p

How much more money
has Max than Minnie? [ ] p

8p

How much will two teddy rubbers cost? [ ] p

How much will three teddy rubbers cost? [ ] p

Number Speed

Try to answer these
questions as quickly
as possible.

8 - 4 =

10 - 7 =

12 - 6 =

15 - 9 =

7 - 3 =

9 - 4 =

14 - 8 =

17 - 6 =

20 - 10 =

20 - 12 =

11 - 5 =

6 - 4 =

20 - 8 =

15 - 6 =

9 - 5 =

19 - 10 =

17 - 9 =

Missing numbers

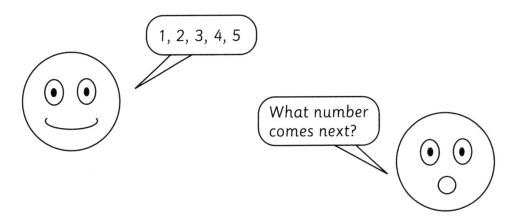

What number comes next?

1)   1,   2,   3,   4,   5, ☐

2)   9,   10,   11,   12, ☐

3)   11,   12,   13,   14, ☐

4)   14,   15,   16,   17, ☐

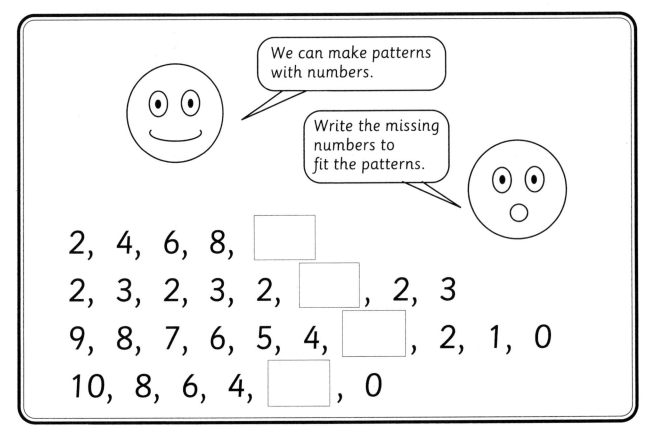

We can make patterns with numbers.

Write the missing numbers to fit the patterns.

2, 4, 6, 8, ☐

2, 3, 2, 3, 2, ☐, 2, 3

9, 8, 7, 6, 5, 4, ☐, 2, 1, 0

10, 8, 6, 4, ☐, 0

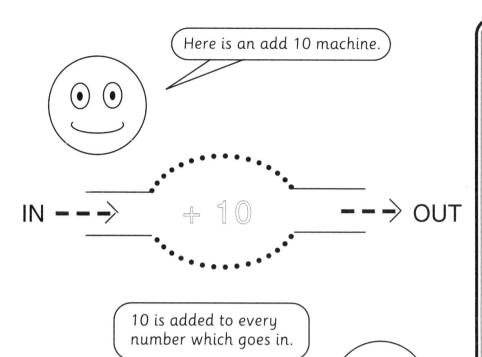

Here is an add 10 machine.

IN ---> + 10 ---> OUT

10 is added to every number which goes in.

Fill in the chart for the add 10 machine:

IN---> + 10 --->OUT

In	Out
6	16
4	
7	
10	
3	
20	
16	

Try to answer these questions as quickly as possible.

10 + 10 =

20 + 10 =

30 + 20 =

30 - 10 =

40 - 20 =

50 + 10 =

50 - 40 =

70 - 10 =

60 - 30 =

12 + 10 =

21 + 10 =

32 + 10 =

10 + 17 =

26 + 10 =

10 + 19 =

10 + 23 =

46 + 10 =

13

Subtraction machines

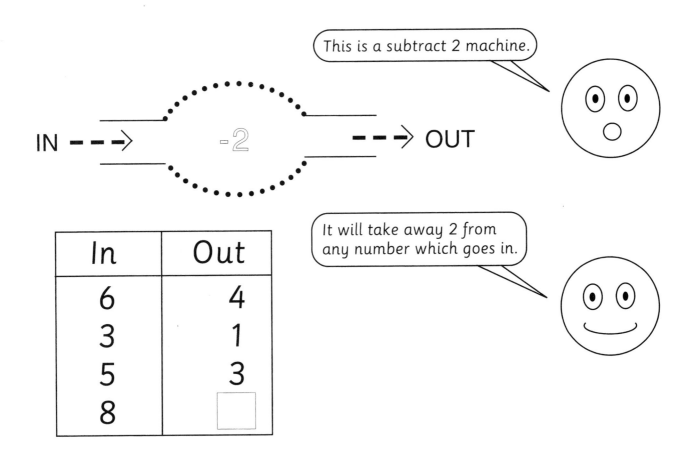

This is a subtract 2 machine.

IN - - → -2 - - → OUT

It will take away 2 from any number which goes in.

In	Out
6	4
3	1
5	3
8	

Fill in the answers for these machines:

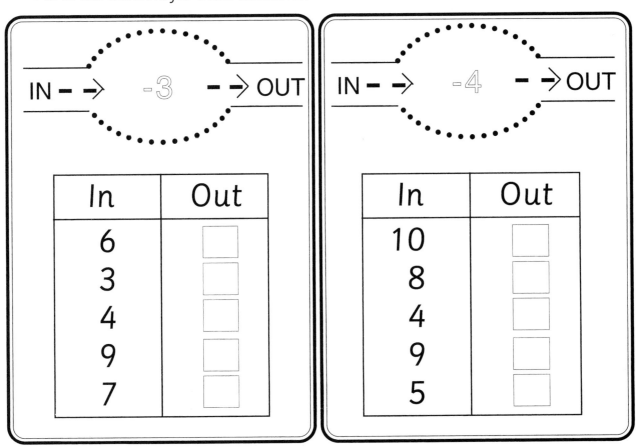

IN - → -3 - → OUT

In	Out
6	
3	
4	
9	
7	

IN - → -4 - → OUT

In	Out
10	
8	
4	
9	
5	

Max and Minnie played a game of darts.

Max scored a ⑤ and a ①.

That's 6 altogether.

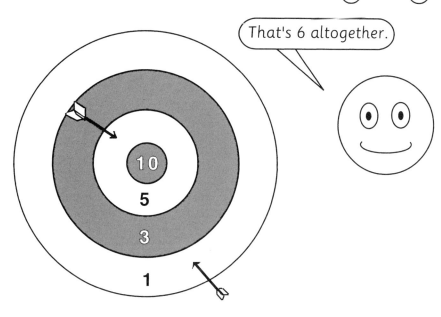

$10 - 5 =$

$9 - 5 =$

$8 - 5 =$

$7 - 5 =$

$6 - 5 =$

$5 - 5 =$

Minnie scored a ⑤ and ③.

That's [ ] altogether.

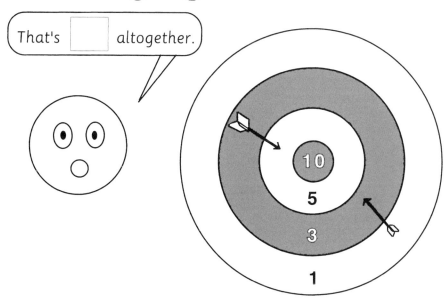

$9 - 6 =$

$8 - 6 =$

$7 - 6 =$

$6 - 6 =$

Who had the highest score?

_____ had the highest score.

$12 - 4 =$

$11 - 4 =$

$10 - 4 =$

How much more was Minnie's score than Max's?

Minnie's score was [ ] more.

$9 - 4 =$

Fractions

A half of this circle is shaded.

We can write half like this: $\dfrac{1}{2}$

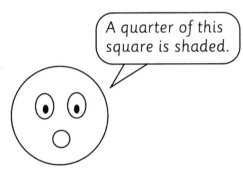

A quarter of this square is shaded.

We can write quarter like this: $\dfrac{1}{4}$

How much of each shape is shaded?

Write $\dfrac{1}{2}$ or $\dfrac{1}{4}$

How much of each shape is shaded?

Write $\frac{1}{2}$ or $\frac{1}{4}$.

6 + 6 =

6 + 5 =

6 + 4 =

6 + 3 =

6 + 2 =

6 + 1 =

6 + 0 =

5 + 0 =

5 + 1 =

5 + 2 =

5 + 3 =

5 + 4 =

5 + 5 =

5 + 6 =

5 + 7 =

①

②

③

④

More fractions

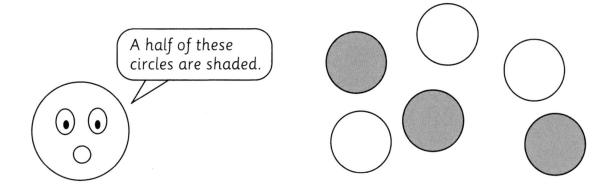

A half of these circles are shaded.

$\frac{1}{2}$ of all these circles are shaded.

$\frac{1}{2}$ of all these circles are not shaded.

In one of these sets, half of the circles are shaded.
Put a tick by the correct set.

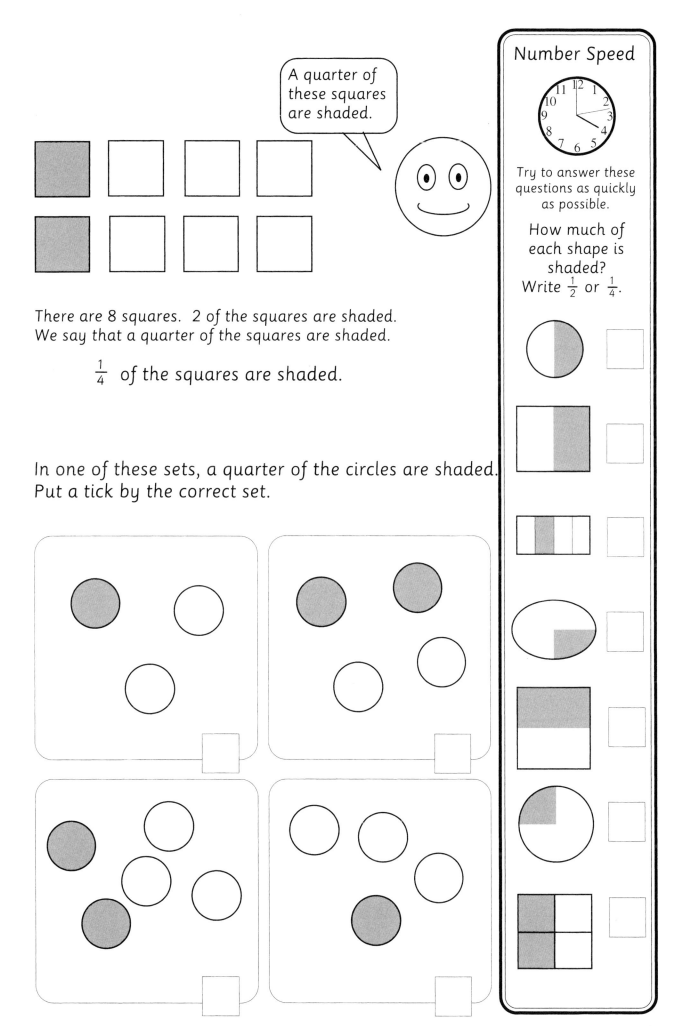

A quarter of these squares are shaded.

There are 8 squares. 2 of the squares are shaded.
We say that a quarter of the squares are shaded.

$\frac{1}{4}$ of the squares are shaded.

In one of these sets, a quarter of the circles are shaded.
Put a tick by the correct set.

Try to answer these questions as quickly as possible.

How much of each shape is shaded?
Write $\frac{1}{2}$ or $\frac{1}{4}$.

Most and Least

At a dog show the dogs were given points by the judges.

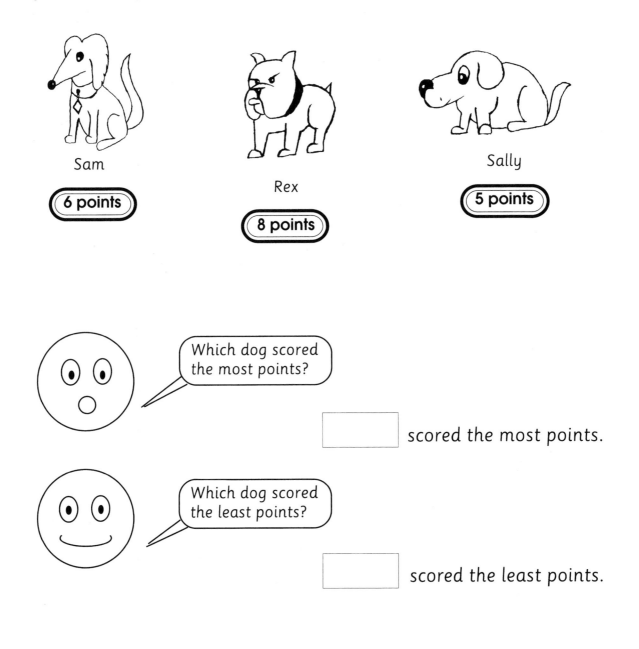

Which dog scored the most points?

[ ] scored the most points.

Which dog scored the least points?

[ ] scored the least points.

Fill in the missing words:

| Rex | came first with | eight | points. |

[ ] came second with [ ] points.

[ ] came third with [ ] points.

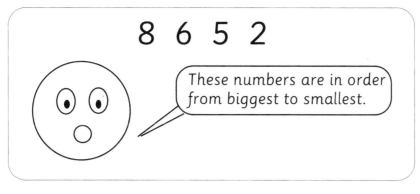

8 6 5 2

These numbers are in order from biggest to smallest.

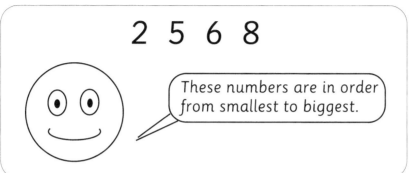

2 5 6 8

These numbers are in order from smallest to biggest.

Write these numbers in order, starting with the smallest:

9 6 4 7

4 ☐ ☐ ☐

Write these numbers in order, starting with the smallest:

3 8 4 2

☐ ☐ ☐ ☐

10 6 1 12

☐ ☐ ☐ ☐

20 10 40 30

☐ ☐ ☐ ☐

15 5 25 10

☐ ☐ ☐ ☐

Multiplication

One set of two stars. —————————————————————▶ 1 x 2 = 2

Two sets of two stars. ————————————————————▶ 2 x 2 = 4

————————————————————————▶ 3 x 2 = 6

————————————————————▶ 4 x 2 = 8

————————————————▶ 5 x 2 = 10

————————————▶ 6 x 2 = 12

————————▶ 7 x 2 = 14

————▶ 8 x 2 = 16

——▶ 9 x 2 = 18

▶10 x 2 = 20

The two times table

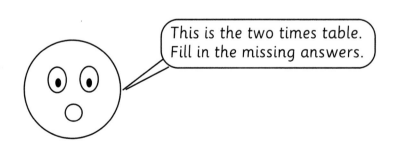

This is the two times table.
Fill in the missing answers.

1 x 2 =

2 x 2 =

3 x 2 =

4 x 2 =

5 x 2 =

6 x 2 =

7 x 2 =

8 x 2 =

9 x 2 =

10 x 2 =

You need to learn the multiplication tables.

Fill in the missing answers in these multiplication tables.
You can count on with your fingers to help you.

The five times table

1 x 5 = ☐
2 x 5 = 10
3 x 5 = ☐
4 x 5 = 20
5 x 5 = 25
6 x 5 = ☐
7 x 5 = 35
8 x 5 = ☐
9 x 5 = 45
10 x 5 = ☐

The ten times table

1 x 10 = 10
2 x 10 = ☐
3 x 10 = 30
4 x 10 = ☐
5 x 10 = ☐
6 x 10 = 60
7 x 10 = ☐
8 x 10 = 80
9 x 10 = ☐
10 x 10 = 100

Number Speed

Try to answer these questions as quickly as possible.

6 x 2 =

4 x 2 =

3 x 5 =

1 x 2 =

2 x 5 =

5 x 2 =

7 x 2 =

5 x 5 =

2 x 2 =

8 x 5 =

9 x 2 =

3 x 2 =

9 x 5 =

4 x 5 =

6 x 5 =

8 x 2 =

Division

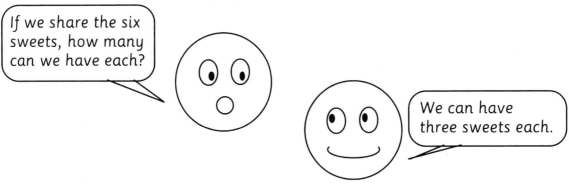

$$6 \div 2 = 3$$

Six divided by two is three.

2 x 3 = 6	2 x 4 = ☐	3 x 3 = ☐
3 x 2 = 6	4 x 2 = ☐	9 ÷ 3 = ☐
6 ÷ 2 = 3	8 ÷ 2 = ☐	2 x 2 = ☐
6 ÷ 3 = 2	8 ÷ 4 = ☐	4 ÷ 2 = ☐

4 x 4 = ☐   3 x 4 = ☐

16 ÷ 4 = ☐   4 x 3 = ☐

5 x 5 = ☐   12 ÷ 3 = ☐

25 ÷ 5 = ☐   12 ÷ 4 = ☐

Try to answer these questions as quickly as possible.

There are eight sweets.

How many sweets can we have each?

Max and Minnie can have ☐ sweets each.

6 ÷ 3 =

12 ÷ 4 =

15 ÷ 5 =

16 ÷ 4 =

8 ÷ 2 =

10 ÷ 2 =

12 ÷ 3 =

15 ÷ 3 =

4 ÷ 2 =

9 ÷ 3 =

8 ÷ 4 =

25 ÷ 5 =

20 ÷ 4 =

10 ÷ 5 =

30 ÷ 3 =

40 ÷ 4 =

5 x 2 = ☐   3 x 5 = ☐

2 x 5 = ☐   5 x 3 = ☐

10 ÷ 2 = ☐   15 ÷ 3 = ☐

10 ÷ 5 = ☐   15 ÷ 5 = ☐

Max and Minnie have 20p to share.
How much can they have each? ☐

25

Measurement

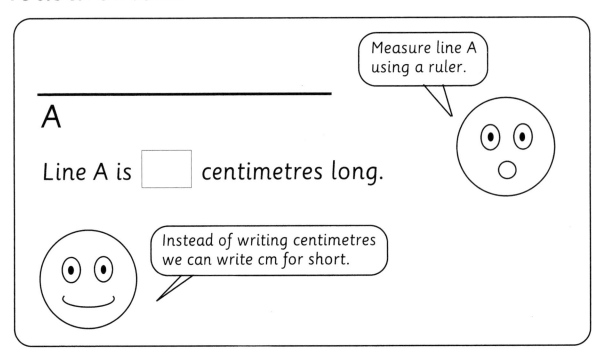

A

Line A is ⬚ centimetres long.

Measure line A using a ruler.

Instead of writing centimetres we can write cm for short.

Measure these lines in centimetres:

B

Line B is ⬚ cm long.

C

Line C is ⬚ cm long.

D

Line D is ⬚ long.

E

Line E is ⬚ long.

F

Line F is ⬚ long.

G

Line G is ⬚ long.

The longest line is line ⬚   The shortest line is line ⬚

Numbers and words

Join the matching pairs.

3   twenty

7   three

15   seven

20   fifteen

twenty-one   18

sixteen   16

nine   21

eighteen   9

Write these numbers in figures:

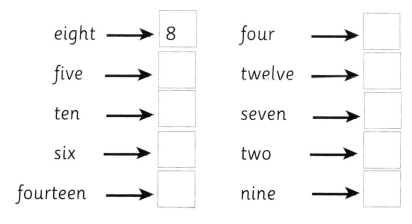

eight ⟶ 8   four ⟶ ☐

five ⟶ ☐   twelve ⟶ ☐

ten ⟶ ☐   seven ⟶ ☐

six ⟶ ☐   two ⟶ ☐

fourteen ⟶ ☐   nine ⟶ ☐

Write the numbers in words:

16 ⟶ ☐

9 ⟶ ☐

17 ⟶ ☐

20 ⟶ ☐

Number Speed

Try to answer these questions as quickly as possible.

$7 + 4 =$

$7 - 3 =$

$3 \times 4 =$

$10 \div 2 =$

$5 + 5 =$

$6 - 4 =$

$5 \times 4 =$

$12 \div 3 =$

$6 + 7 =$

$9 - 3 =$

$2 \times 5 =$

$6 \div 3 =$

$8 + 4 =$

$12 - 7 =$

$5 \times 5 =$

$9 \div 3 =$

More addition

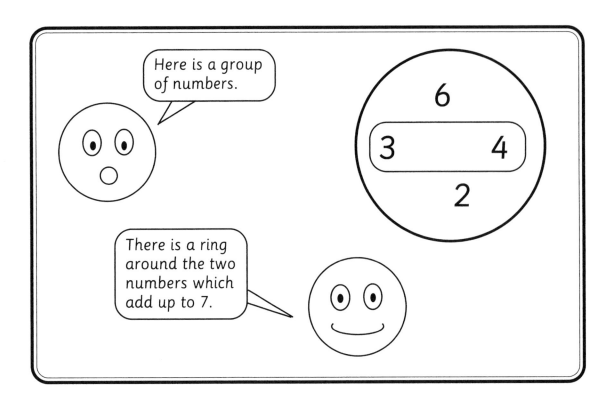

Draw a ring around the two numbers which add up to 8.

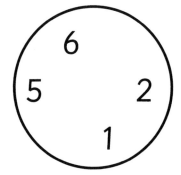

Draw a ring around the two numbers which add up to 6.

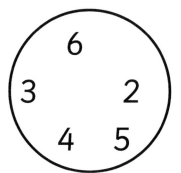

Draw a ring around the two numbers which add up to 9.

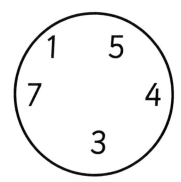

Draw a ring around the two numbers which add up to 10.

Complete these additions.

16 + 3 = ☐

12 + 5 = ☐

14 + 4 = ☐

11 + 3 = ☐

8 + 7 = ☐

13 + 3 = ☐

15 + 13 = ☐

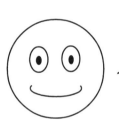

Complete these subtractions.

17 − 9 = ☐

14 − 6 = ☐

11 − 2 = ☐

15 − 7 = ☐

12 − 8 = ☐

19 − 16 = ☐

13 − 7 = ☐

If Max has 25p and Minnie has 12p, how much more has Max got than Minnie?

Max has got ☐ p more than Minnie.

More time

What times are shown on the clocks?

Half past three

Half past

Quarter past four

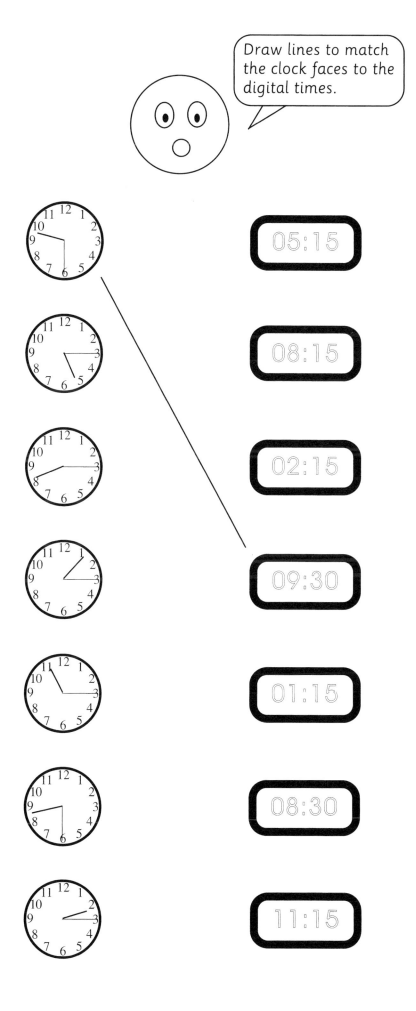

Draw lines to match the clock faces to the digital times.

05:15

08:15

02:15

09:30

01:15

08:30

11:15

$\frac{1}{2}$ of 6 =

$\frac{1}{4}$ of 8 =

$\frac{1}{2}$ of 10 =

$\frac{1}{2}$ of 12 =

$\frac{1}{4}$ of 12 =

$\frac{1}{2}$ of 4 =

$\frac{1}{4}$ of 4 =

$\frac{1}{2}$ of 2 =

$\frac{1}{4}$ of 16 =

$\frac{1}{2}$ of 16 =

$\frac{1}{2}$ of 20 =

$\frac{1}{4}$ of 20 =

$\frac{1}{2}$ of 18 =

$\frac{1}{2}$ of 14 =

$\frac{1}{2}$ of 100 =

31

Shopping

Apples 6p each

Bananas 8p each

Oranges 7p each

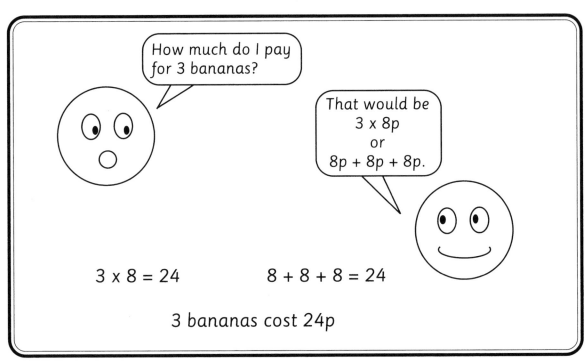

Work out these costs:

2 apples cost [ ] p   3 oranges cost [ ] p

2 bananas cost [ ] p   4 apples cost [ ] p

3 apples cost [ ] p   2 oranges cost [ ] p

3 apples and 2 oranges cost [ ] p altogether.

1 apple, 1 banana and 1 orange cost [ ] p altogether.

2 apples, 2 bananas and 2 oranges cost [ ] p altogether.

If I bought a banana and an apple how much change would I have from 20p?

 A banana and an apple cost 14p altogether so the change from 20p is 6p.

Try to answer these questions as quickly as possible.

20 - 10 =

20 - 18 =

20 - 2 =

20 - 7 =

20 - 15 =

20 - 20 =

20 - 8 =

20 - 6 =

20 - 0 =

20 - 16 =

20 - 5 =

20 - 12 =

20 - 17 =

20 - 9 =

20 - 3 =

20 - 1 =

Two oranges cost ☐ p.
The change from 20p is ☐ p.

An apple and an orange cost ☐ p altogether.
The change from 20p is ☐ p.

Two bananas and two oranges cost ☐ p altogether.
The change from 50p is ☐ p.

One banana costs ____ p
Two apples cost ____ p
Three oranges cost ____ p
They cost ____ p altogether.

The change from 50p is ☐ p.

Two bananas cost ____ p
One apple costs ____ p
Two oranges cost ____ p
They cost ____ p altogether.

The change from 50p is ☐ p.

Graphs

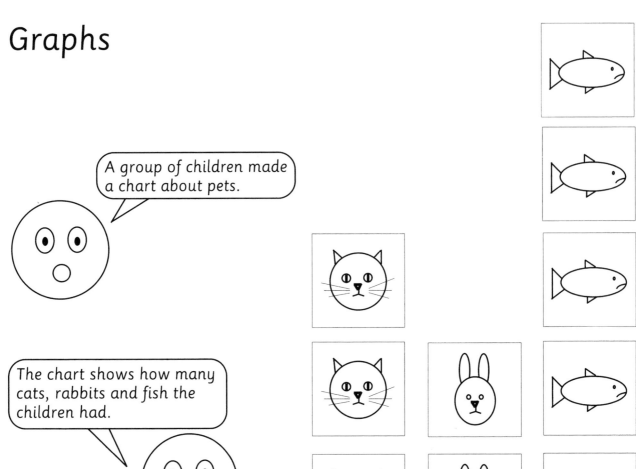

Cats   Rabbits   Fish

Look at the chart to answer these questions:

Which type of pet was the most popular?

How many more cats than rabbits were there?

How many more fish than cats?

How many fewer rabbits than fish?

How many pets were there altogether?

The children counted vehicles passing by.

They made a bar-chart to show their results.

Try to answer these questions as quickly as possible.

$1 \times 2 =$

$2 \times 2 =$

$3 \times 2 =$

$4 \times 2 =$

$5 \times 2 =$

$1 \times 3 =$

$2 \times 3 =$

$3 \times 3 =$

$4 \times 3 =$

$5 \times 3 =$

$1 \times 4 =$

$2 \times 4 =$

$3 \times 4 =$

$4 \times 4 =$

$5 \times 4 =$

$0 \times 3 =$

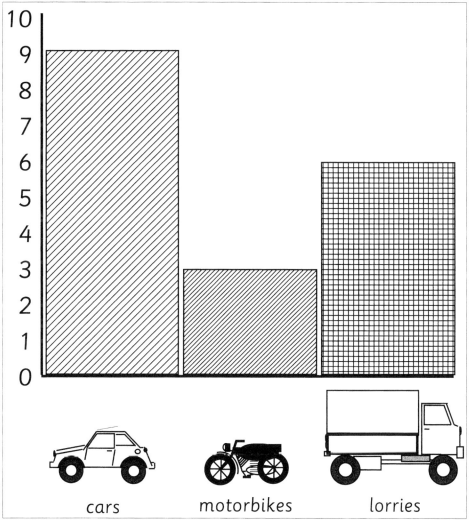

cars   motorbikes   lorries

How many cars passed by? ☐

How many lorries passed by? ☐

How many motorbikes passed by? ☐

How many more cars than lorries passed by? ☐

How many fewer motorbikes
        than cars passed by? ☐

Shapes

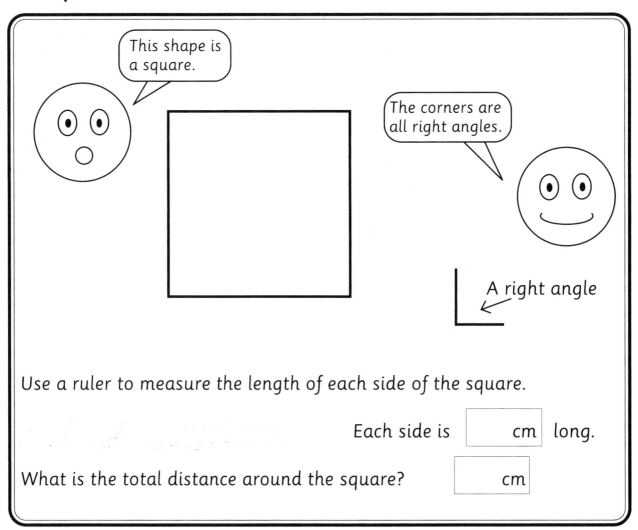

Use a ruler to measure the length of each side of the square.

Each side is [ ] cm long.

What is the total distance around the square? [ ] cm

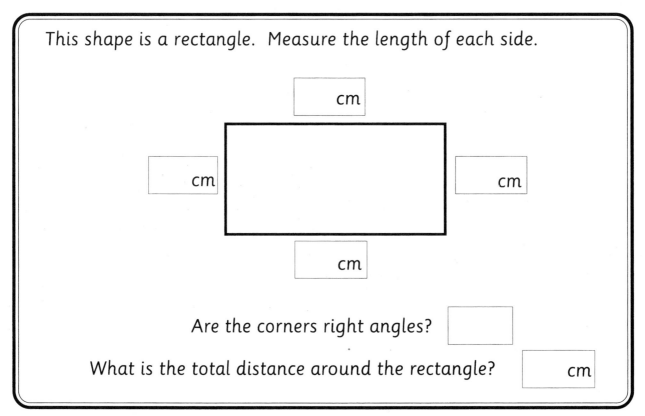

This shape is a rectangle. Measure the length of each side.

Are the corners right angles? [ ]

What is the total distance around the rectangle? [ ] cm